STOP PULLING BACKWARDS. LOOK WHAT HAPPENED TO THAT DOG.

WHY ARE YOU PUTTING ALL THOSE PATCHES ON YOUR BIKE TYRE?
WELL, IF I GET A PUNCTURE, IT WILL BE ALREADY MENDED!

I THINK I'LL RETIRE. HE'S GIVEN ME TWO BLACK EYES.
SO WHAT? HE CAN'T GIVE YOU ANY MORE!

WHAT ARE YOU DOING, FATTY?
ER—JUST PUTTING A FEW THINGS AWAY, BRAINY.
CHEESE

£2·40

HANDS OFF!
THIS BOOK BELONGS TO–
Veronica Ryric
1 Samphery road Lang
stracht
Tel 690969

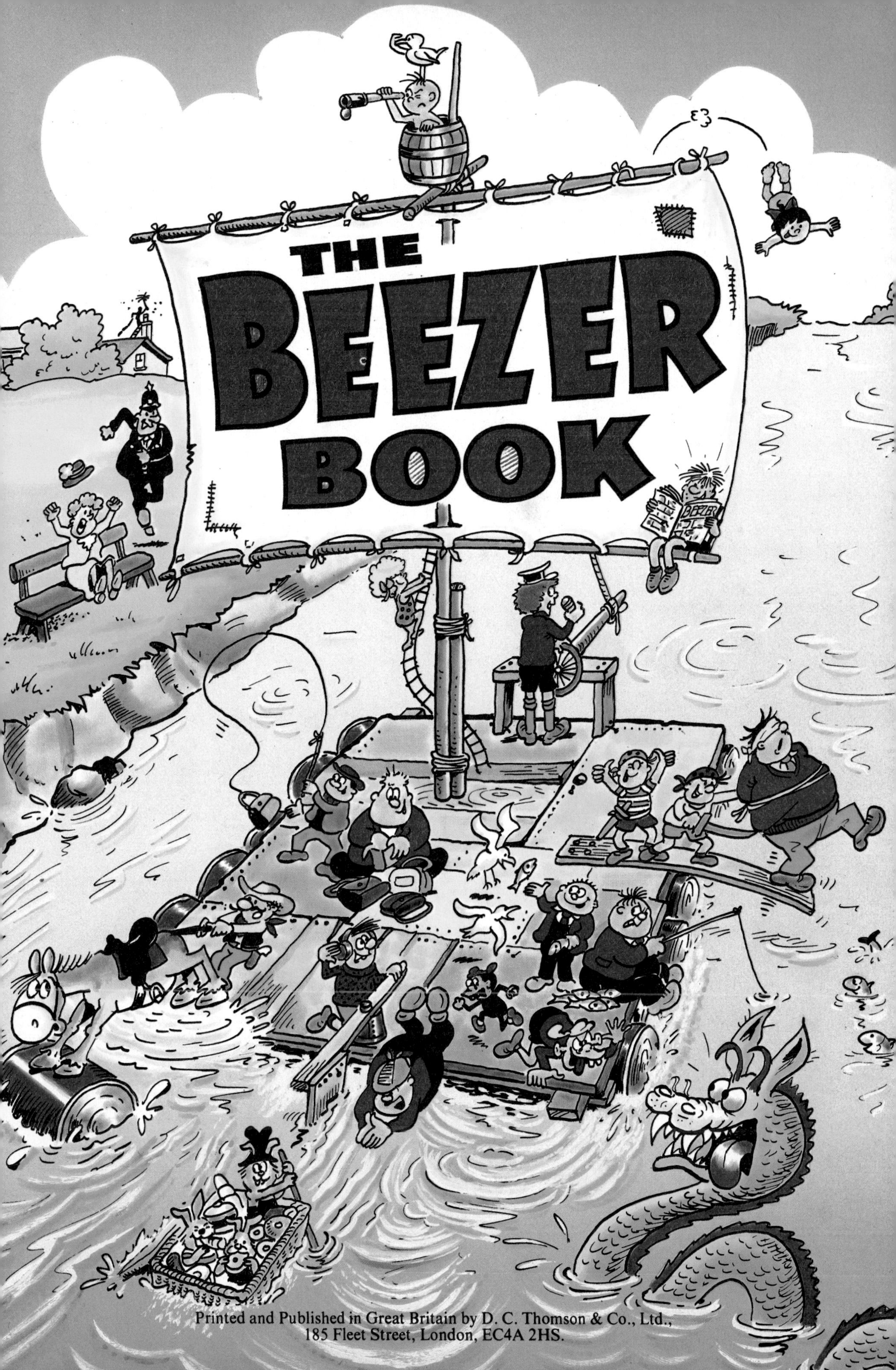

Printed and Published in Great Britain by D. C. Thomson & Co., Ltd.,
185 Fleet Street, London, EC4A 2HS.

A shower of fun with the red-haired one!

Then—
WHEE! THERE'S ANOTHER ONE.

Just then—
WATCH WHERE YOU'RE GOING.
BUMP!
OOF!

USE THAT SHOWER.
HM!

BAH! IT'S NOT WORKING!
HO-HO!
HA-HA!

THUD!
WORK, YOU USELESS THING!
HOI! STOP TRYING TO WRECK THE PLACE.

GET DRESSED AND LEAVE!
OO-ER! I'M JUST GOING!

Minutes later—
EXIT
HUH! I REALLY WANTED A SHOWER.

Suddenly—
WHOOPS! SORRY!
GROOH!

Then—
AARGH!
OH, DEAR! SORRY! I DIDN'T SEE YOU.

And—
EEK!

At the exit door—
OH, NO! THIS IS THE LAST STRAW!

WHAT ARE YOU SO ANGRY ABOUT? IT'S ONLY A SHOWER.
WAAGH!

Things don't go well at this hotel.

THE BADD LADS

I'LL GRAB THIS TURKEY.
LET'S SEE—THAT'S TURKEY FOR TABLE FOUR AND . . .

PULL!
ZUNK!
OUCH! I'VE GRABBED THE TABLECLOTH, TOO!
HOI!

OUT!
BOOT!

Later—
THIS IS THE PANTRY WINDOW. I'LL CLIMB IN AND GRAB SOME POSH NOSH, LADS.
BRING ME A CHICKEN!
HOTEL

But—
HELP! I'M STUCK!
!

NOT FOR LONG, MATE!
!

MIGHTY SHOVE!
DUCK!
IT WAS A CHICKEN I WANTED, NOT A DUCK!
HOTEL

PARKLAND HOTEL
RESTAURANT OPEN TO POSH NON-RESIDENTS
IT'S NO USE, BOSS. WE DON'T LOOK POSH ENOUGH. WE'LL JUST HAVE TO EAT IN SOME CRUMMY CAFE.
PAINFUL LANDING
I'VE GOT IT! KNUCK, HERE'S A POUND. GO AND HIRE SOME POSH DINNER SUITS FOR US.
GREAT IDEA, BOSS!

Later, at the hideout—
YOU FOOL! I TOLD YOU TO HIRE POSH DINNER SUITS, NOT ARAB ROBES!
BUT THAT'S ALL I COULD GET FOR A POUND!
NOT TO WORRY, BOSS. WE COULD PRETEND TO BE RICH OIL SHEIKS.
HIRE CO.

Several thumps from the doorman later—

A froggie's tea doesn't appeal to Baby C!

BABY CROCKETT

You'll laugh a lot at Pop's robot!

MY MECHANICAL DOG NEVER NEEDS TO BE FED.
BULLY FOR HIM!
TOWSER

And in the living room—
LOOK, TWINS. TOWSER'S NEVER BROUGHT ME MY SLIPPERS.
HUH! WHAT A SHOW-OFF!

But then—
BAH! I CAN'T GET IT TO DROP MY SLIPPERS!

GRR! LET GO, YOU MECHANICAL MENACE!
POOR POP'S HAVING TROUBLE WITH HIS PET.

HEE-HEE! TOWSER MAY NOT HAVE BROUGHT YOU YOUR SLIPPERS, BUT HE DIDN'T RIP THEM IN HALF, EITHER!
EEK!

GRR! I DIDN'T MAKE THAT TIN DOG TO BRING SLIPPERS—I MADE IT TO BE A GUARD DOG. I'LL SHOW YOU!

I'LL PUT THIS ON THE LAWN.

NOW I'LL GO BACK INSIDE AND WAIT FOR A THIEF TO COME ALONG!

Soon after—
THERE HE IS! GO GET HIM, TINRIBS!

But then—
OUCH!
HO-HO! THAT TIN TWIT'S BITING POP INSTEAD OF CHASING THE THIEF!

OH, NO! HELP!

CALL IT OFF, SOMEBODY!
HEY! WHERE'S THE GRANDFATHER CLOCK?
THERE IT GOES, MUM!
HA-HA! IT'S A DOG'S LIFE, POP!
CHOMP!
CRUNCH!

Dan makes a mistake when he tries to bake.

BEEFY DAN
THE FAST-FOOD MAN

DAN, YOU'RE GETTING LAZY! HOW ABOUT MAKING SOME COOKIES?
YAH! MISSED AGAIN!
PEANUTS

So—

I'VE MADE COOKIES LIKE THE BOSS SAID.

PHEW! THEY'RE MIGHTY HEAVY!

Shortly—

AH! DAN'S MADE COOKIES AND LEFT THEM OUT TO COOL. I'LL TRY ONE.

But—

WOW! WHAT A WEIGHT!

THOSE COOKIES WERE LIKE LEAD! MAKE THEM LIGHTER!

So—
THIS LOT WILL BE LIGHTER.
Then—
I'LL POP 'EM IN THE OVEN TO BAKE.
But later—
HEY! WHO'S STOLEN MY COOKIES?
Then—
OH, THERE THEY ARE. HOW'D THEY GET UP THERE?
I'LL TAKE 'EM OUT TO COOL!
Just then—
I'LL CATCH THAT PESKY MOUSE YET!

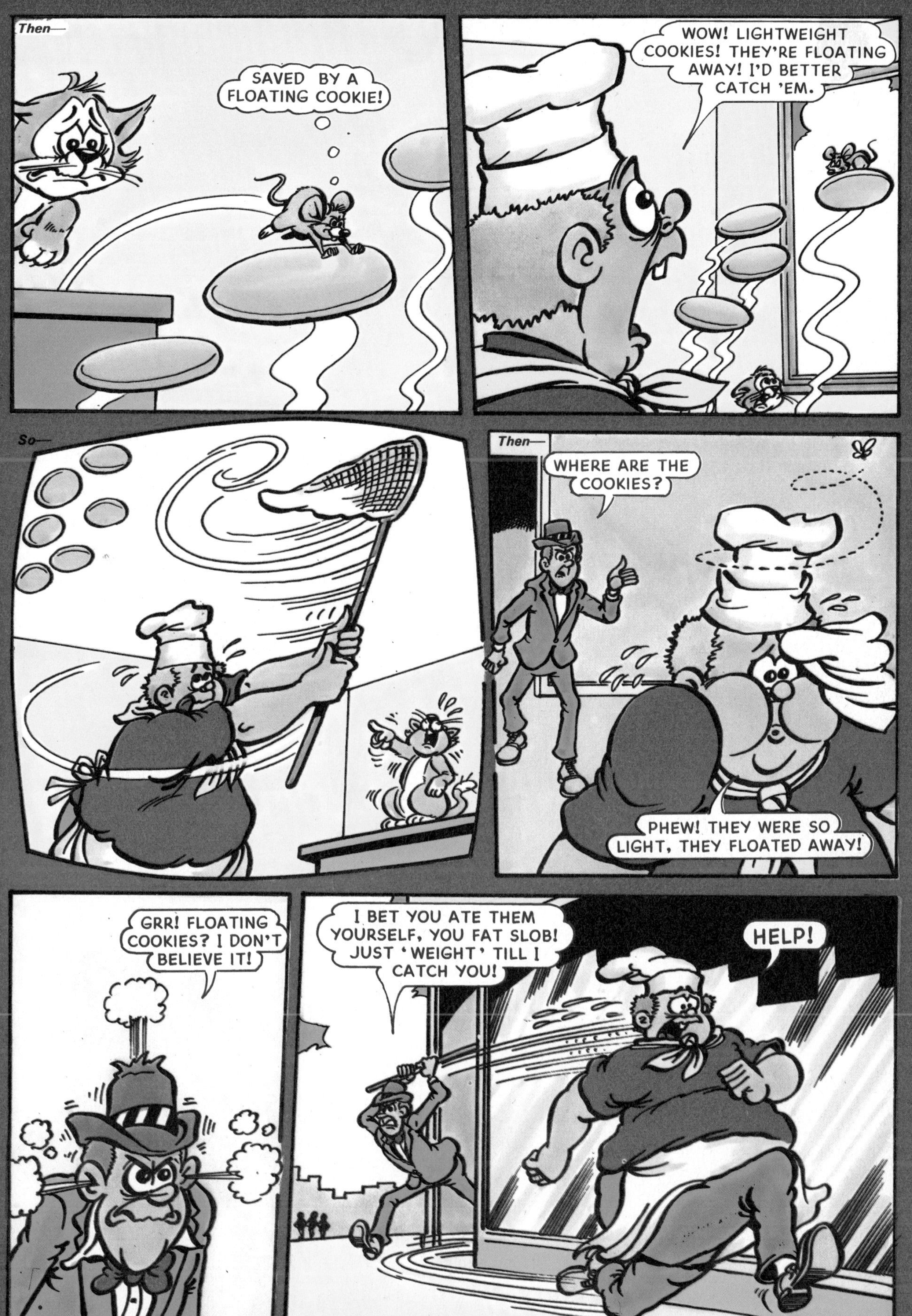
Then—
SAVED BY A FLOATING COOKIE!
WOW! LIGHTWEIGHT COOKIES! THEY'RE FLOATING AWAY! I'D BETTER CATCH 'EM.
So—
Then—
WHERE ARE THE COOKIES?
PHEW! THEY WERE SO LIGHT, THEY FLOATED AWAY!
GRR! FLOATING COOKIES? I DON'T BELIEVE IT!
I BET YOU ATE THEM YOURSELF, YOU FAT SLOB! JUST 'WEIGHT' TILL I CATCH YOU!
HELP!

Hoss as a bird? Now that's absurd!

Later, in town—
I'VE GOT A NICE BOWL OF FOOD FOR THE BIRDS.

Outside—
CHIRP! CHIRP!
WOW!

HELLO! IS THAT THE ZOO? THERE'S AN UNUSUAL SPECIMEN OF BIRD OUTSIDE. IT'S PROBABLY DOWN FROM THE MOUNTAINS. IT EATS LIKE A HORSE!

Meanwhile—
THIS IS LOVELY GRUB!

But then—
HEY! WHAT'S GOING ON?

CHIRP! NEIGH! CHIRP!
STORE
ZOO
HM! THAT SOUNDS LIKE HOSS IN THAT ZOO TRUCK!

ZOO
I'D BETTER GO AND SEE WHAT HOSS HAS BEEN UP TO.

And—
HA-HA! IT MAKES A CHANGE FOR ME TO BE GETTING YOU OUT FROM BEHIND BARS, BIRD-BRAIN.
BAH! THIS REALLY GIVES ME THE BIRD.
DO NOT FEED

Just take a look at this ' scrap '-book!

SCRAPPER

LOOK! HERE'S THE DIARY I'VE KEPT SINCE THE FIRST OF JANUARY.
DIARY

I HAD TO CLEAR AWAY SNOW—NOT EXACTLY SPIFFING FUN!

HO-HO! BUT I HAD LOTS OF 'BIFFING' FUN.

EEK!
OW!
HELP!
THERE WERE A LOT OF FALLS IN FEBRUARY.

HOI!
HEY!
YES! AND I CAUSED MOST OF THEM!

MY HAT!
I THOUGHT THE WIND WOULD NEVER STOP BLOWING IN MARCH.

OOF!
I GOT IN A FEW GOOD 'BLOWS' MYSELF.

IT RAINED ALL THROUGH APRIL.

YEAH! AND I 'RAINED' PUNCHES ON BASHER BILL.

BAH! ALL I DID WAS DIG, DIG, DIG IN MAY.

OW!
I GAVE LANKY LANE A GOOD 'DIG' IN THE RIBS.

ICE CREAM
IT WAS TOO HOT IN JUNE.

WELL, I COOLED A FEW PEOPLE DOWN.

I DID ENJOY GOING FOR A PADDLE IN THE RIVER IN JULY.

I DID A BIT OF 'PADDLING', TOO.

AUGUST WAS A DISASTROUS TIME FOR ME WITH MY CRICKET BAT.

HO-HO! I THINK I WAS A BIG HIT WITH MINE.

EVERYTHING WAS DAMP AND MISERABLE IN SEPTEMBER.

ESPECIALLY TUBBY TATE AFTER I KNOCKED HIM INTO A PUDDLE!

I WASN'T ANY GOOD DUCKING FOR APPLES AT THE HALLOWE'EN PARTY IN OCTOBER.

ORCHARD
WHEE! BEEFY BROWN WASN'T MUCH GOOD AT 'DUCKING' EITHER.

MY GUY DIDN'T EARN MUCH IN NOVEMBER.
PENNY FOR THE GUY

PENNY FOR THE GUY.
MINE DID! IT WAS SO LIFE-LIKE—THANKS TO PETE HELPING ME!

I GOT NOTHING BUT THINGS TO WEAR AT CHRISTMAS.

WHEE! NEW BOXING GLOVES!
SO DID I.

TAKE THAT!
OW!
AND I HAD A GREAT TIME TRYING THEM OUT.

BAH! I THINK THE PAST YEAR HAS BEEN TERRIBLE.
WELL I DON'T! IN FACT, I THINK IT HAS BEEN A REAL 'KNOCKOUT'!

PUZZLE

1—This colourfully-dressed gentleman is properly known as a Yeoman of the Guard and can be seen guarding the Crown Jewels in London. Do you know his more familiar nickname? Is it: (a) Beefeater? (b) Grenadier Guard? (c) Royal Archer?

2—Flies beware! This plant actually feeds on small insects. It attracts them with its sweet smell and traps them on its sticky leaves. Is it a: (a) Bee Orchid? (b) Spotted Flycatcher? (c) Sundew?

3—Isn't this a strange creature? About eighteen feet long, it lives in the Arctic Ocean, and its huge tusk is thought to be used for defence. It feeds on squid, fish, prawns and shrimps. Is it a: (a) Porpoise? (b) Killer Whale? (c) Narwhal?

4—You won't see many people riding these today! It was one of the early forms of bicycle. Is it called a: (a) Boneshaker? (b) Penny Farthing? (c) Tandem?

5—If you lift up a flat stone, you might find this fearsome-looking beetle. But don't be alarmed. It is harmless—and doesn't have a sting in its tail! Is it a (a) Devil's Coach Horse? (b) Colorado Beetle? (c) Deathwatch Beetle?

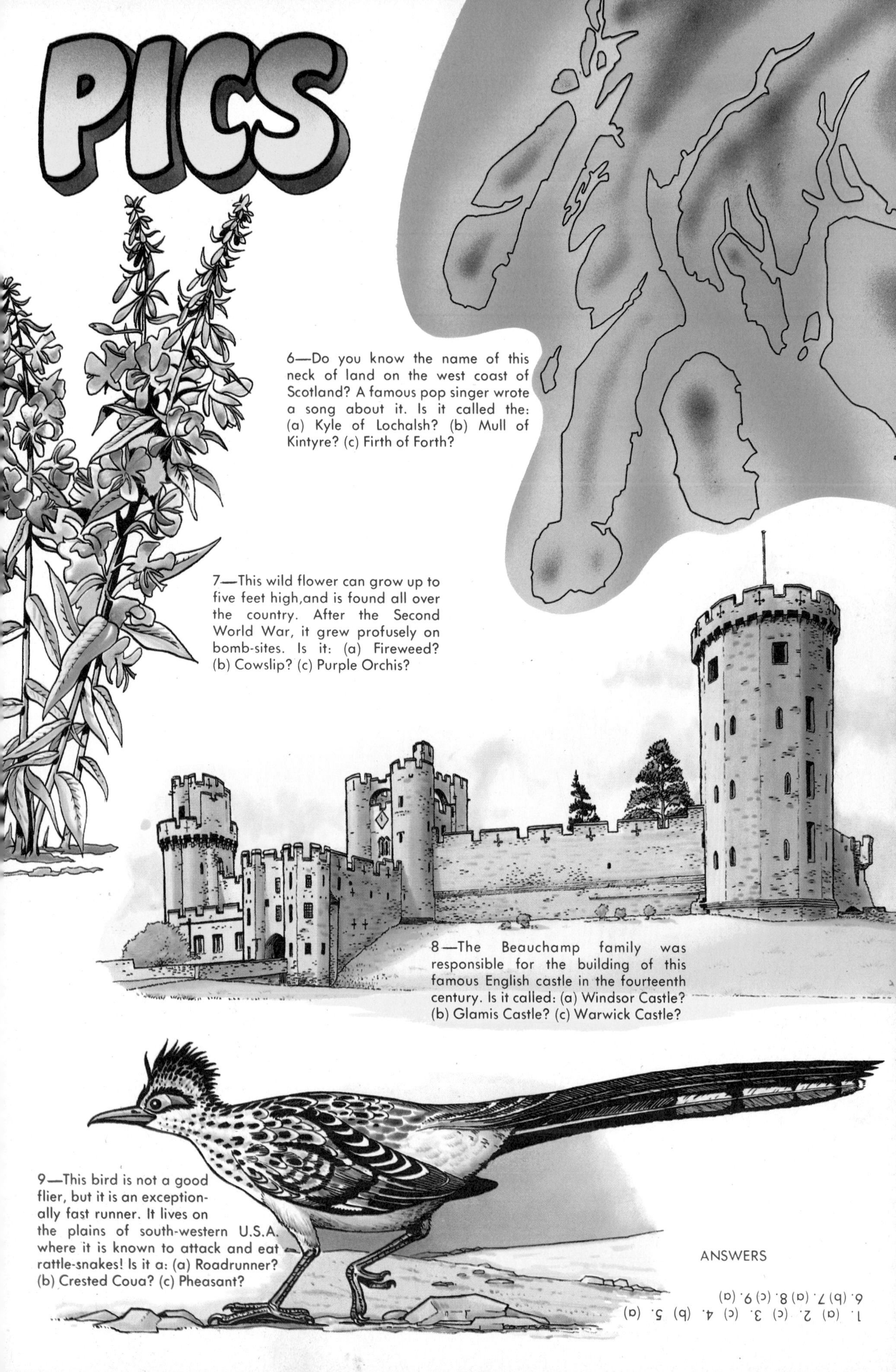

PICS

6—Do you know the name of this neck of land on the west coast of Scotland? A famous pop singer wrote a song about it. Is it called the: (a) Kyle of Lochalsh? (b) Mull of Kintyre? (c) Firth of Forth?

7—This wild flower can grow up to five feet high,and is found all over the country. After the Second World War, it grew profusely on bomb-sites. Is it: (a) Fireweed? (b) Cowslip? (c) Purple Orchis?

8—The Beauchamp family was responsible for the building of this famous English castle in the fourteenth century. Is it called: (a) Windsor Castle? (b) Glamis Castle? (c) Warwick Castle?

9—This bird is not a good flier, but it is an exceptionally fast runner. It lives on the plains of south-western U.S.A. where it is known to attack and eat rattle-snakes! Is it a: (a) Roadrunner? (b) Crested Coua? (c) Pheasant?

ANSWERS

1. (a) 2. (c) 3. (c) 4. (b) 5. (a)
6. (b) 7. (a) 8. (c) 9. (a)

The fun sure is good — Fatty's looking for food!

LET ME IN, YOU ROTTERS! I'M HUNGRY!

Later—
I'M TUNNELLING MY WAY INTO THE PANTRY.

But—
AARGH!
WAAH! THE FLOOR'S OPENING UP. IT MUST BE AN EARTHQUAKE!

HEY! IT ISN'T AN EARTHQUAKE. IT'S FATTY! I'LL BET HE WAS TRYING TO TUNNEL INTO THE PANTRY.
WE'LL FIX HIM THIS TIME, LADS. I'LL FETCH THE PLUNGER.

So—
HO-HO! LET'S SEE IF WE CAN UNBLOCK THAT TUNNEL.
GOOD IDEA, BRAINY!

RIGHT, LADS, DON'T PUSH UNTIL I TELL YOU TO!

HOI! WHAT'S THAT?

RIGHT, LADS— PUSH!
AAAARGH!

Fatty shoots out of the tunnel and lands on the bedspring.
WAAH!

AAAA—

—AARGH!

Inside the hut—
OH, NO! HE'S LANDED IN THE PANTRY!
PANTRY
MUNCH!
MUNCH!
GET HIM OUT BEFORE HE SCOFFS OUR GRUB!

GULP! I CAN'T. THE DOOR'S LOCKED AND I'VE LOST THE KEY!
YOU CLOT! WE CAN'T EVEN BURST THE DOOR OPEN!

HO-HO! I CAN EAT AS MUCH AS I WANT. THE BUNCH CAN'T GET IN TO STOP ME!

Meanwhile—
GRRR! COME BACK HERE!
STEADY ON, LADS! LOSING THE KEY WAS AN ACCIDENT!

A laughter treat when old pals meet!

The NUMSKULLS

So—

Then—

Then—

But—

Soon—
THE RAIN'S GETTING HEAVIER. I'LL BE SOAKED BY THE TIME I GET TO THE REUNION.

Then—
I'LL TELL HIM TO TAKE A SHORTCUT.
BRAIN DEPT.
TAKE SHORT-CUT THROUGH BUILDING SITE!
SUGGESTION BOX

So—
I'LL TAKE A SHORTCUT THROUGH HERE.
BUILDING SITE

But then—
AARGH!

Some time later—
I USED TO BE A REAL FATTY UNTIL I WENT ON A DIET.
PEOPLE CAN'T CALL ME SKINNY ANY MORE. I TOOK UP BODY BUILDING.
AND I LOST ALL MY CURLY HAIR.
I'M SMILEY. BUT I LOST ALL MY TEETH.

Then—
WE'VE ALL CHANGED A LOT —BUT THERE'S SOMETHING THAT'S STAYED THE SAME.

HA-HA! LOOK AT THE MESS HE'S IN. HE WAS ALWAYS THE SCRUFFIEST BOY AT SCHOOL.
YEAH! HE DIDN'T GET CALLED 'SCRUFFY' FOR NOTHING.

AH, WELL! HE GAVE EVERYONE A GOOD LAUGH. HEE-HEE!
HA-HA!
HA-HA!
AND WE HAD A GOOD TIME, TOO.

Fruit hoot!

Little
MO

HERE'S AN ORANGE, MO.
COO! TA, MUM!

I'M GOING TO ENJOY THIS.

But then—
EEK!
HAR! GOT YOU!

I'LL GET MY OWN BACK ON MUGSY FOR THAT!

HEH! MO'S LEFT HER ORANGE. I'LL HAVE IT!

Then—

JUST AS I THOUGHT! HE'S GOING TO PICK UP MY ORANGE.

And—
BULL'S-EYE!
SPLAT!
GROOH!

I HOPE YOU ENJOYED MY ORANGE, MUGSY! HO-HO!

A tale about cheese that's sure to please!

BEEFY DAN
THE FAST-FOOD MAN

THOSE HAMBURGERS SMELL GOOD, DAN.
I'M GLAD YOU LIKE 'EM, BOSS.

I'LL LEAVE THIS LOT HERE WHILE I FRY SOME MORE.
COO! GRUB! I'LL TELL THE OTHERS.

And—
YUM! I CAN'T WAIT TO GET STUCK INTO THIS LOT.

Soon—
I'M LOOKIN' FORWARD TO THIS BURGER.

Suddenly—
MUNCH! THIS IS DELICIOUS!

Then—
I HEAR SOMEONE SNORING.
IT'S COMING FROM YOUR HAMBURGER.
ZZZZ

THAT'S FUNNY. IT'S STOPPED.

Suddenly—
CAN'T A MOUSE SLEEP IN PEACE?
OW!

Then—
I HEAR MUSIC.

WHEE! LET'S DANCE!
ERK! MICE!

THIS CHEESE WILL ATTRACT THE MICE.

But—
GLUMF!

Then—
LEMME AT THAT CHEESE!
LEMME AT THOSE MICE!

THERE'S ONLY ONE THING TO DO— RUN!

DAN SEEMS TO BE A BIT 'CHEESED' OFF, BUT AT LEAST HE'S GOT RID OF THE MICE! HO-HO!

Mum gets mad at her scruffy lad!

I'LL JUST HAVE TO CLEAR THE TABLE WITHOUT TOUCHING THE DISHES WITH MY HANDS!

I'LL LIFT THEM WITH MY MOUTH INSTEAD.

Then—
SMIFFY, GET YOUR MOUTH OFF THAT PLATE.
OO-ER, OKAY, MUM!

I KNOW! I'LL CARRY THE TABLE INTO THE KITCHEN ON MY BACK!

HO-HO! THIS IS A GREAT IDEA!

But—
OH, NO! THE TABLE'S TOO WIDE TO FIT THROUGH THE DOORWAY. NEVER MIND! I HAVE ANOTHER IDEA!

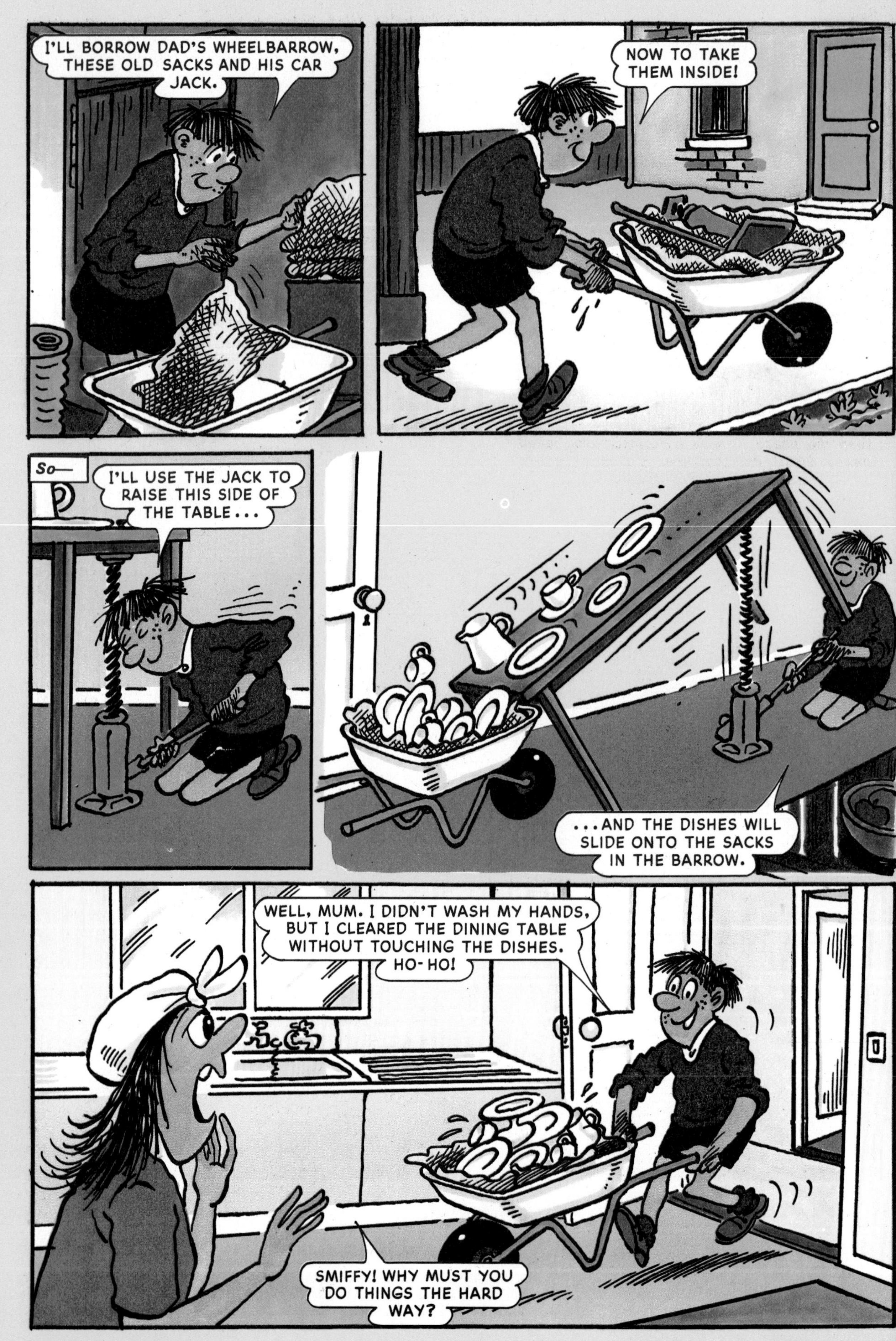
I'LL BORROW DAD'S WHEELBARROW, THESE OLD SACKS AND HIS CAR JACK.
NOW TO TAKE THEM INSIDE!
So—
I'LL USE THE JACK TO RAISE THIS SIDE OF THE TABLE...
...AND THE DISHES WILL SLIDE ONTO THE SACKS IN THE BARROW.
WELL, MUM. I DIDN'T WASH MY HANDS, BUT I CLEARED THE DINING TABLE WITHOUT TOUCHING THE DISHES. HO-HO!
SMIFFY! WHY MUST YOU DO THINGS THE HARD WAY?

OUR SHERIFF'S AN APE!

COYOTE CREEK *is normally a nice, quiet town in the Wild West for it has two sheriffs to keep the peace. One is a normal bloke called Danny Blain—but the other is Danny's pet, a huge ape called Charlie.*

BE A BIT MORE CHOOSEY ABOUT YOUR STAFF, MISTER CREEDY. THAT'S THE SECOND TIME THIS WEEK THAT CHARLIE'S FOUND WANTED CRIMINALS WORKING FOR YOU!

BUT THOSE TWO ARE MY COOKS.
CROOKS, YOU MEAN! THEY'RE WANTED FOR ROBBERY.

JUST BE A BIT MORE CAREFUL OR I'LL CLOSE YOUR PLACE DOWN.
GRR! HIM AND THAT OVERGROWN MONKEY ARE GETTING TOO BIG FOR THEIR BOOTS.

Catching crooks is very hungry work and Charlie had only one thought on his mind as he patrolled the town later that day—food!

Suddenly, the huge ape's eyes opened wide. Someone had been dropping bananas.
YUM-YUM!

Charlie's long strides ate up the ground—and he ate up the bananas!

At last he came to the end of the trail.

In more ways than one! A blow on the head knocked him cold.
And when Charlie recovered he was frussed up like a turkey.
JUST YOU STAY THERE, YOU BIG APE.
HUH?

Some time later, Blinky Bradley was stumbling up a dark alley.

Suddenly—
IS THAT YOU, CHARLIE? WHAT HAVE YOU BEEN DOING IN THE BANK?

That's when Blinky found out the meaning of 'hard cash'! The hairy thief swung his bag of loot and Blinky went out like a light!
OW!

Meanwhile, Danny was getting a bit anxious about his pal.
I WONDER WHERE CHARLIE IS. IT'S NOT LIKE HIM TO BE LATE.

I'LL HAVE TO GO AND LOOK FOR HIM.

Then—
WOW! WHAT'S THIS? HEY! IT'S OLD BLINKY BRADLEY!

WHAT HAPPENED, OLD-TIMER?
MY BANK!
I CAUGHT CHARLIE COMING OUT OF THE BANK AND HE BASHED ME OVER THE HEAD.

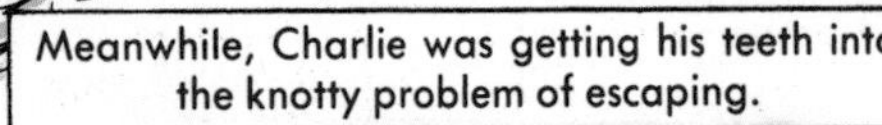

The bank manager rushed into his office and lit a lamp. Then—

Meanwhile, Charlie was getting his teeth into the knotty problem of escaping.

Now no one makes a monkey out of Charlie and gets away with it. He raced out of his prison shack, determined to find his attacker. Instead, he found the posse!
THERE'S THE BANK ROBBER NOW. ARREST HIM.
CHARLIE!

So—
JUST HOLD IT RIGHT THERE, CHARLIE. I'LL HAVE TO PUT YOU IN JAIL UNTIL I GET TO THE BOTTOM OF THIS.
HUH?

Soon the hairy sheriff was locked up in a tiny cell.
NOW, DON'T CAUSE ANY TROUBLE. I'VE GOT A LOT OF INVESTIGATING TO DO.

Charlie was miserable. No one seemed to believe he was innocent.

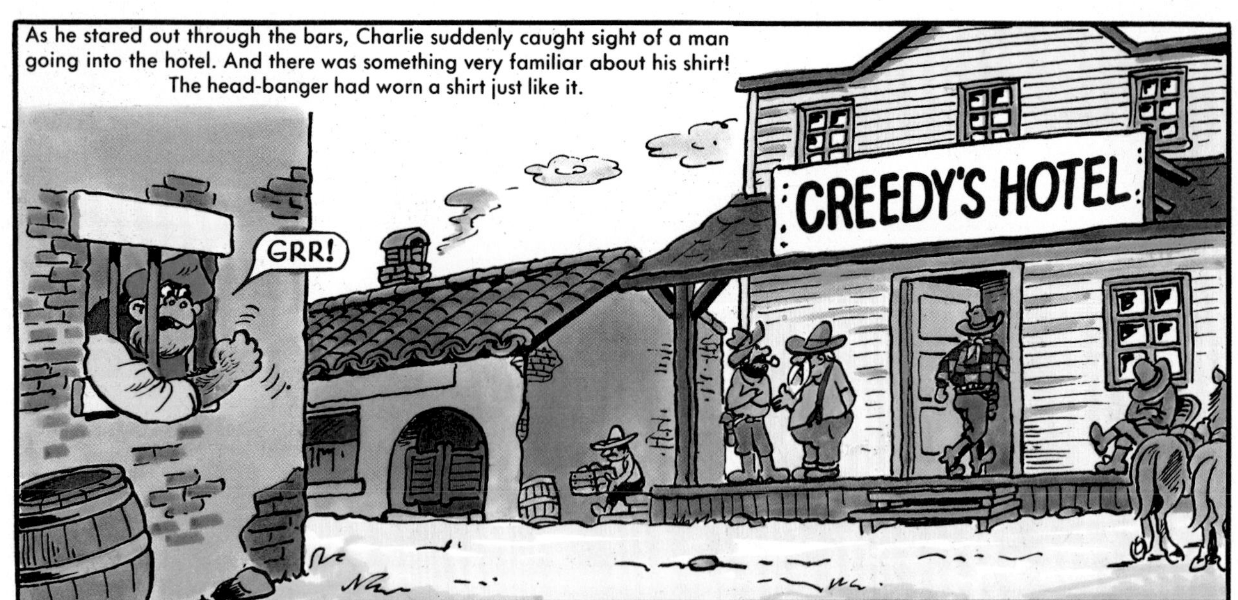
As he stared out through the bars, Charlie suddenly caught sight of a man going into the hotel. And there was something very familiar about his shirt! The head-banger had worn a shirt just like it.
GRR!
CREEDY'S HOTEL

The huge ape was determined to catch the man and no cell was going to hold him back, so—
UMPH!

Then—
HEY! HOW DID HE GET OUT OF JAIL?

The angry sheriff stormed into the hotel. But then—
IT'S THAT APE! FILL HIM FULL OF LEAD!

Charlie was as hard as iron, but he didn't fancy stopping any lead. He took to his heels.

With bullets whizzing round his ears, he leapt into the saddle of a horse hitched to a rail.

Charlie gave a tug on the reins— and the whole rail came loose!

HE'S LET MY HORSE FREE. WHOA, TRIGGER!

In the confusion that followed, the jail-breaker made good his escape.

EEK!
OW!
HELP!
WHAT HIT ME?
WHOA!

Charlie headed for the hills. He was in big trouble and he needed time to think.

He also needed food. He searched in the saddlebags of the horse he had 'borrowed'.

That's when he found the bananas! He was just going to gobble them up when a thought struck him. They were the same kind as the ones that he had been following!
BADLAND'S BANANAS

Charlie put two and two together and came up with a very painful answer.
+
BADLAND'S BANANAS
=

The horse clearly belonged to the crook with the club, so Charlie slapped it with a banana skin and off it ran. The ape hoped it would lead him to the crook's hideout.

The horse headed straight back towards town. Charlie raced after it. He had to see where it finally stopped.
COYOTE CREEK

And that's when he got a shock. The nag pulled up outside Creedy's hotel!
CREEDY'S H

The hairy sheriff couldn't risk going in the front door again so he decided to find a back way into the hotel.

Then—
HO-HO! WE GOT THOUSANDS OF DOLLARS FROM THE BANK AND EVERYONE THINKS THAT CHARLIE DID IT, MISTER CREEDY.

THAT'S RIGHT, MICK—THANKS TO YOU CLOBBERING CHARLIE AND ME WEARING THIS APE SKIN!
HA-HA!

Charlie had seen enough. He shinned up a nearby tree.

He swung his powerful body up . . .

. . . and then down! Straight through the window.
AAGH!
AAIIEEE!

Danny Blair was searching for clues when he heard roars and squeals of pain.
SOMEBODY'S IN TROUBLE! LET'S GO.
GRR!
HELP!
OW!
GRR!
EEK!

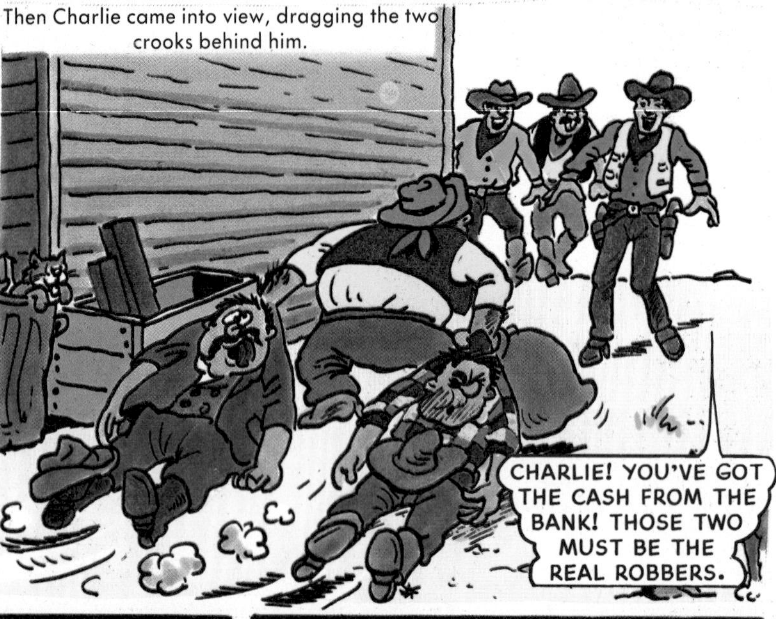
Then Charlie came into view, dragging the two crooks behind him.
CHARLIE! YOU'VE GOT THE CASH FROM THE BANK! THOSE TWO MUST BE THE REAL ROBBERS.

When Danny found the ape skin he knew what had happened. Charlie was completely innocent! The bank manager was delighted to get his money back and—
HERE'S A LITTLE REWARD. YOU'LL BE ABLE TO BUY YOURSELF SOME BANANAS.

But Danny had other plans for the reward money.
SORRY, CHARLIE BUT YOU DAMAGED THE JAIL. THIS'LL HELP TO PAY FOR IT.
BAH!

Lots of mishaps with burglar traps!

But when he presses the doorbell—

And—
TOPPLE
GLUG!

THUNK!

Then—
THERE'S BEEN PLENTY OF NOISE, JIM. LET'S TAKE A LOOK.

WHEE! WE'VE CAUGHT THE BURGLAR!

Later—
WE'VE CAUGHT THE BURGLAR, SARGE!
POLICE
WELL DONE, SID!

But—
D-DAD! HOW DID YOU GET THERE?
GRRR!
COO! P.C.99.
POLICE

Here's a silly billy! He thinks chili's chilly!

HUNGRY HOSS

LOOK! ZE-GRINGO HORSE EES DANCING!

I MUST FIND WATER!
HEH-HEH! WE'VE CAUGHT YOU AT LAST, JOE!

AH! A HORSE TROUGH!

Soon—
I'M STILL REALLY HOT—HEY! JOE'S BEEN CAUGHT BY THE SHERIFF!

POOR GRINGO JOE! ZEY TAKE HIM TO ZE COOLER!
EH?

Then—
GREAT! HERE COMES HOSS TO RESCUE ME!

But—
SHUCKS! HOSS WANTS TO BE ARRESTED!
YEP! TAKE ME TO THE COOLER!
BAH!

Later—
WHY DO THEY CALL THIS PLACE THE COOLER? I'M NO COOLER THAN I WAS WHEN I ATE THAT CHILI.
JAIL
Maybe it's because the food isn't too hot, eh, Hoss?

‘ Water ’ hoot with the silly old coot!

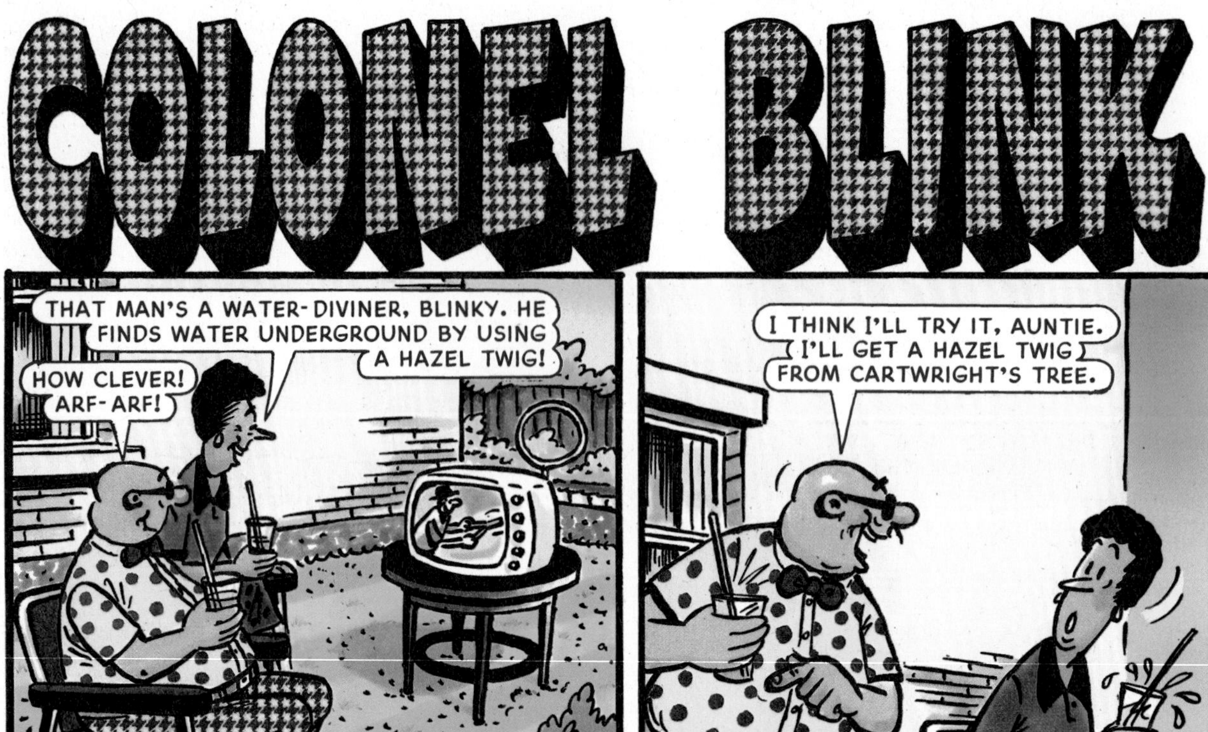

That hook's catching Blinky's shoe.

Suddenly—

Soon after—

BEEZER
REDHWARA
TRIFUNERU
TRINOTSETARY
INOTSETARY
ARFOWTOE
TRELELACI
OYTS
1
2
3
4
5
6
2—Mo and Mirabelle are admiring the table lamps. There is a design on each shade which changes in a certain pattern from left to right. See if you can work out what design should be on the fourth lamp.
1—Ginger wants to take the lift to the toy department upstairs but he doesn't know which floor it's on because the names are jumbled up. Can you help him unscramble them?
3— Six little Numskulls are hidden on these pages. See if you can find them.
4—The Beezer artist has made 10 deliberate mistakes in drawing this Santa's Grotto. Can you spot them?
SANTA'S GROTTO
COMPUTAR GAMES
SNAKES & LADDERS
DRAUGHTS

TEEZERS

5—Dick and Harry are helping Pop look for the Menswear department. Turn 'Mens' into 'Wear' in four moves, changing one letter each time to form a new word.

6—Blinky thinks these dummies all look the same, but only two are, in fact, identical. Which two?

7—The Bunch only have enough money for one pair of socks. Brainy thinks the one who has the fewest number of pairs should get the new socks. He has one pair less than Tiny who has two pairs more than Fatty. Dopey has one pair more than Lanky and two pairs less than Tiny. If Brainy has 5 pairs who should get the socks?

ANSWERS

1—Hardware; Furniture; Stationery; Footwear; Electrical; Toys.

2— 

3—Inside shade of table lamp on left side of table; In cab of toy lorry; At window of doll's house; Beside Pop's foot; Behind Blinky's legs; Between Tiny and Dopey.

4—Santa has one boot and one shoe; United Kingdom is upside down on globe; Guard has rifle upside down; Doll has three legs; Door on doll's house is upstairs; Wrong number of squares on draught board; Computer spelled wrongly; Steering wheel in rear seat of car; Cowboy facing wrong way on horse; Sails wrong way round on yacht.

5—Mens—Tens—Teas—Tear—Wear, is one way of doing it.

6—3 and 5 are identical.

7—Lanky. He has the fewest pairs of socks.

Laughs for you with Saucy Sue!

SAUCY
SUE

I'M GOING TO THE BIG GAME WITH GRANDAD. THERE'S BOUND TO BE A BIG CROWD.

Inside—
IT CAN GET COLD AT A FOOTBALL MATCH, GRANDAD. YOU'D BETTER PUT PLENTY OF CLOTHES ON.
OH! OKAY, SUE!

And—
ARE YOU SURE I'LL NEED ALL THOSE CLOTHES ON, SUE?
WELL, ONE OF US MIGHT!

At the football ground—
WE'LL GET A GREAT VIEW FROM UP HERE, SUE.
HM! I'M NOT SO SURE!

And—
JUST AS I THOUGHT. I CAN'T SEE A THING. THIS ALWAYS HAPPENS TO ME!

Then—
IT'S NOT AS COLD AS I, THOUGHT, GRANDAD. MAYBE YOU SHOULD TAKE OFF A FEW THINGS.
PHEW! I'LL HAVE TO. I'M STEWING!

I'LL TAKE OFF MY BIG OVERCOAT.

AND MY SMALL OVERCOAT.

AND MY JACKET.
COMIC

AND I THINK I'LL TAKE OFF ONE OF MY CARDIGANS.

THAT'S BETTER. AYE, IT'S A GRAND VIEW FROM UP HERE, EH, SUE?

IT CERTAINLY IS, NOW THAT I'VE GOT A DECENT HIGH SEAT!
COMICS

Smiffy has a lucky break — and no mistake!

Smiffy

SMIFFY, GO AND COLLECT MY VASE FROM AUNTIE MAY, AND DON'T BREAK IT.
OKAY, MUM!

And so—
BE CAREFUL GOING HOME WITH YOUR MUM'S VASE, SMIFFY!
DON'T WORRY, AUNTIE MAY.

But then—
OH, NO!

UNLESS I JUMP OUT OF THE WAY, THOSE CYCLISTS WILL RUN ME OVER.
ROAD UP

PHEW! I MOVED JUST IN TIME!
ROAD

AND MUM'S VASE IS STILL IN ONE PIECE!
ROAD UP

Soon after—
HEY! WHAT'S THAT, SMIFFY?
ER ... IT'S A VASE, BASHER!

THEN GET RID OF IT, YOU SOFTY! HO-HO!

WAAH! IF THAT VASE BREAKS, MY MUM'LL THUMP ME!
GOOD! HEH-HEH!

CAUGHT IT! THAT'S A RELIEF!

Minutes later—
HOME AT LAST!

HERE'S YOUR VASE, MUM, AND I DIDN'T BREAK IT!
SMIFFY, YOU'RE FILTHY!

GIVE THAT VASE TO ME!
CAREFUL, MUM!
GRAB

But—
OH, NO!
SMASH

MUM WARNED ME NOT TO BREAK THE VASE AND ENDED UP DOING IT HERSELF. HO-HO!

A tick-tock shock!

Next day at dawn—
WE'VE NO AMMUNITION LEFT SO WE'LL INVITE THEM BILLYS TO JOIN OUR CLUBS. HEE-HEE!

But—
HEY! THERE'S SOMETHING TICKING!
TICK! TICK!
MAYBE IT'S A BOMB!

WOW!
LET'S GET OUTA HERE!
TICK! TICK!
WHAT'S GOING ON?

WOW! IT'S TICKING!
A BOMB!
TICK! TICK!

Later—
HO-HO! NOT A HILLY OR A BILLY IN SIGHT.
HA-HA! THEY DON'T KNOW IT'S JUST A CLOCK! I'VE STOPPED THEM FEUDIN'!
A CLOCK? WE'VE BEEN TRICKED.

Then—
PAW! IT'S A TRICK! THE SHERIFF PUT A CLOCK IN THE BOX!
WHAT?

LET'S PLAY A TRICK, TOO.

HO-HO! THIS REAL DYNAMITE WILL CATCH THE HILLYS NAPPING!

IT'S JUST A TRICK! THERE'S ONLY A CLOCK IN THE CRATE! COME OUT AND FIGHT.

BAH! THEY'VE RUMBLED MY TRICK.

HO-HO! I FOOLED YOU ALL. BUT IT WAS NICE AND QUIET FOR A WHILE.

BOOM!

BAH! ANY MORE GOOD IDEAS, SHERIFF?
NOW WE CAN FEUD IN PEACE!

You're sure to grin when the Bunch sleep in!

YOU GET DOPEY DOWN. I'LL GET FATTY OUT OF THE BARREL!
HELP!

COME ON, FATTY! GET DRESSED!
WAAH!

Minutes later—
TEACHER WARNED US YESTERDAY NOT TO BE LATE AGAIN!
SCHOOL
LET'S HOPE HE'S IN A GOOD MOOD!
But he isn't!
YOU'LL EACH DO TWO HUNDRED LINES FOR TOMORROW!
ROTTER!

After school—
WE'LL HAVE TO BUY A NEW ALARM CLOCK SO THAT WE DON'T SLEEP IN TOMORROW!
I HAVE A BETTER IDEA. WE'LL BORROW FARMER BROWN'S COCKEREL!

Later—
LET'S HAVE AN EARLY NIGHT! THE COCKEREL WILL WAKEN US UP AT DAWN!
GOOD IDEA, BRAINY!

Come dawn—
YOUR PLAN WORKED, BRAINY. WE'RE ALL AWAKE BRIGHT AND EARLY.
COCK-A-DOODLE-DO
RIGHT! LET'S GET UP AND DO OUR LINES!

Much writing later—
I'VE FINISHED! IT'S TIME FOR SCHOOL NOW!
LET'S GO!

And so—
MORNING, SIR! HERE ARE THE LINES YOU ASKED FOR!
WELL DONE, BOYS!
Later—
HO-HO! THE BUNCH WERE UP SO EARLY THAT THEY'VE FALLEN ASLEEP.
WAKEN UP, BOYS!

YAWN! IS IT TIME FOR SCHOOL ALREADY?
NO! IT'S TIME TO GO HOME!

GRR! TEACHER GAVE US MORE LINES TO DO BECAUSE WE FELL ASLEEP IN CLASS!
IT'S BRAINY'S FAULT! THAT COCKEREL WOKE US UP TOO EARLY!

Smoke joke!

The MUNCHERS

Down below—
COUGH! START DIGGING! I'VE AN IDEA.

Much digging later—
NOW LET'S HEAD FOR THE SURFACE.

And—
PERFECT! RIGHT UNDER FARMER'S WIFE'S WASHING.

Meanwhile—
HAR! THEM MUNCHERS SHOULD APPEAR ANY SECOND NOW.

But—
TAKE THAT, YOU FOOL!
BAM!

LOOK WHAT YOU'VE DONE! YOU'LL HAVE TO DO THE WASHING AGAIN!

NEE-HEE! FARMER'S PLANS TO CATCH US HAVE GONE UP IN SMOKE!

Peace and quiet turn into a riot!

The NUMSKULLS

And—
LET'S LIE IN THE SUN, TOO, LADS.
GOOD IDEA, BRAINY.

Soon—
EVEN IF THAT RABBIT LANDS ON OUR MAN AGAIN, WE WON'T GET TOSSED ABOUT.

But suddenly—
AAGH!
GROOH!

YOU IDIOT! YOU SOAKED ME.
SORRY, OLD MAN. I WAS JUST WATERING MY GARDEN.

FOLLOW ME! I'M GOING TO TELL OUR MAN TO BUILD A FENCE.
WHY DON'T YOU TELL HIM TO GO INTO THE HOUSE?

Then—
BRAIN DEPT.
A BIG FENCE WILL KEEP EVERYONE OUT.
IT SEEMS A LOT OF HARD WORK. I STILL THINK HE'D BE BETTER SITTING IN THE HOUSE.
BUILD A FENCE. HAMMER FENCE POSTS IN FIRST
SUGGESTION BOX

But—
I'D BETTER HAMMER STOUT POLES INTO THE GROUND FIRST.

So—
HERE GOES.

Oh-oh! Look what's happening!

And—
OH, NO! I'VE HIT A WATER PIPE.

Minutes later—
WHAT AN IDIOT!
I'LL START THE SUCTION PUMP.
MAKING A SWIMMING POOL?
BAH! SO MUCH FOR A BIT OF PEACE AND QUIET.
FIRE SERVICE
STAND BACK, FOLKS.
POLICE
POLICE
WATER BOARD
WE'LL HAVE TO DIG UP HIS GARDEN TO PUT IN A NEW PIPE.

GRR! IT'S EVEN NOISIER THAN EVER IN THE GARDEN.
YEAH! AND IT WON'T BE ANY QUIETER INSIDE THE HOUSE WITH ALL THOSE PEOPLE AROUND.
WHAT A FOOL YOU ARE, BRAINY.

JOE SOAP
JOE BROWN was known as Joe Soap by the people in Sudbury. You see, he was forever blowing amazing bubbles from mixtures made by his grandfather, a real crackpot inventor.
One day, when Grandad's out in the garden—
MY MARROWS ARE SURE TO WIN A PRIZE AT THE LOCAL SHOW.
THOSE SKINNY THINGS OF YOURS DON'T STAND A CHANCE.
BOASTER BATES IS RIGHT.
I'LL SEE IF I CAN MAKE A MIXTURE THAT'LL BOOST THE SIZE OF OUR MARROWS.
Soon—
HERE GOES! MY MARROWS WILL GROW IN A FLASH.
Just then, Joe opens the garden gate and—
SPLOSH!
OOPS! SORRY, GRANDAD.
Suddenly—
FLASH!
OH, NO!

YOU CLUMSY CLOT! YOU'VE MADE ME TURN INTO A PARROT.
WELL KEEP YOUR FEATHERS ON, GRANDAD. THE SPELL WILL WEAR OFF EVENTUALLY.
Just then—
EEK! THERE'S A BIRD AFTER THE MARROWS.
So—
SHOO! CLEAR OFF!
SQUAWK! AARGH!
STOP SQUAWKING AND FLY.
Later—
I'M PECKISH, JOE.
WELL, YOU CAN'T GO HOME LOOKING LIKE THAT.
FRUIT &
Then—
I'LL NIP IN HERE AND NICK A FEW GRAPES.
WHEE! I'M GOING TO ENJOY THIS.

But then—
OOPS! I THOUGHT I WAS LANDING ON A COCONUT!
OH, NO! LOOK WHAT HE'S DONE.
ORANGES
FRESH FARM EGGS.
OOF!
Then—
BUZZ OFF!
ER—JUST GOING!
Soon after—
HM! THERE'S A BAG OF NUTS. THAT'S BETTER THAN NOTHING.

So—
MMPH! THIS ISN'T AS EASY AS IT LOOKS.
SNAP
Suddenly—
HO-HO! YOU WERE TOO HEAVY, GRANDAD.
SPLOOSH!!
BIRD BRAIN!
BRR! THE WATER'S FREEZING.
CHATTER!
So—
I'LL MAYBE GET A HEAT FROM THAT CHIMNEY POT.

But—
OH, NO! HE'S FALLEN DOWN THE CHIMNEY.
CRA-A-ACK!
Fortunately there's no fire in the grate and—
WHUMPH!
WHAT WAS THAT, ALF?
BAH! IT'S JUST SOME STUPID BIRD FALLING DOWN THE CHIMNEY.
LET'S CARRY ON WITH OUR PINCHING.
EH? THEY'RE A COUPLE OF CROOKS.
And—
HELP!
POLICE!
THAT BIRD WILL BRING THE COPS ALONG.

SHUT UP, YOU NOISY PEST. OOPS!
CRASH!
YAH! MISSED.
But the vase doesn't miss Joe!
CLUMP!
OOYAH!
Then—
I'LL CALL THE POLICE ON THE PHONE.
OH-OH!
IT'S TIME WE BEAT IT, BERT.
EMERGENCY! SEND THE FLYING SQUAD!
Joe gets in the way again, and—
OOF!
HURRY UP, ALF. GET ON THE BIKE.

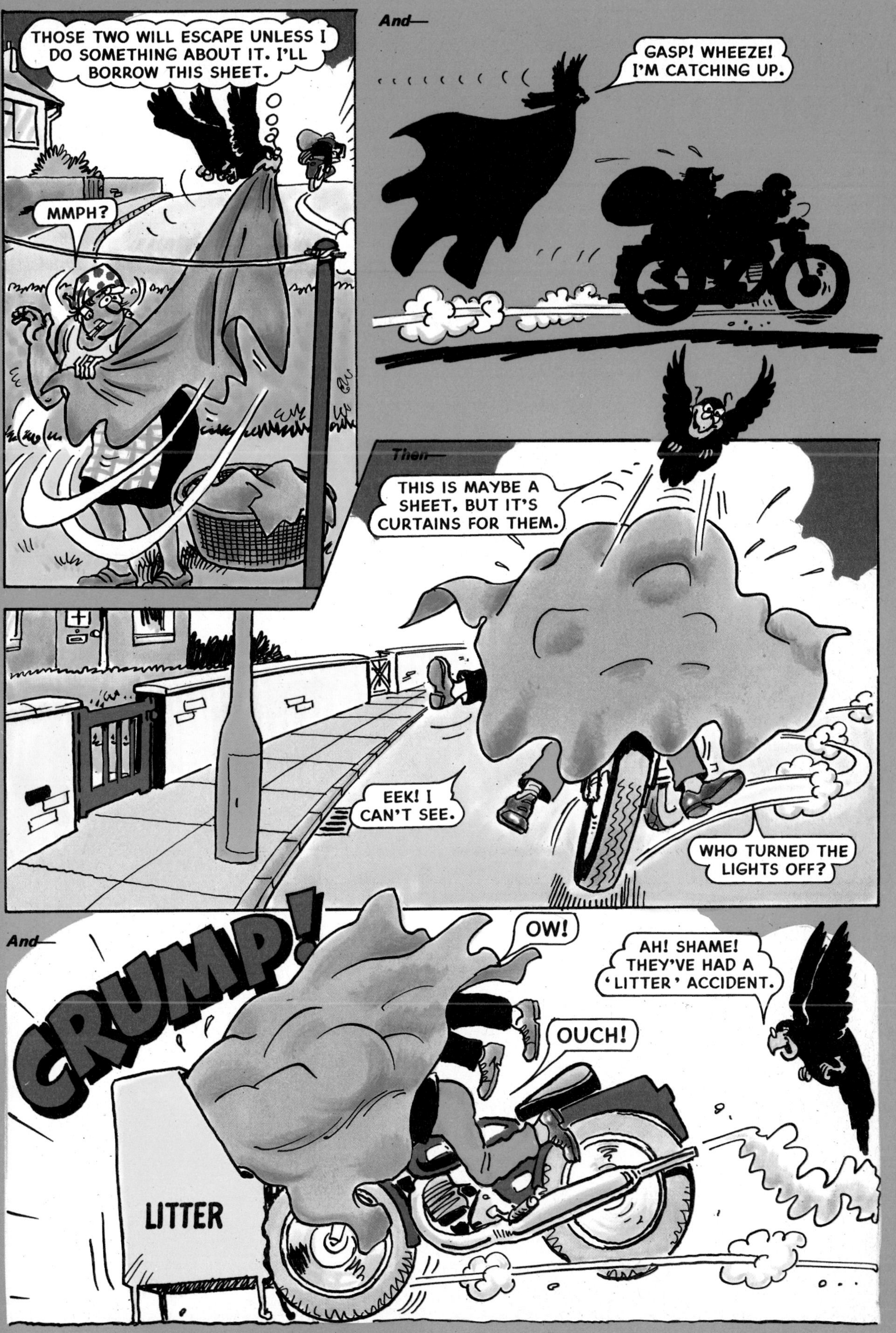
THOSE TWO WILL ESCAPE UNLESS I DO SOMETHING ABOUT IT. I'LL BORROW THIS SHEET.
MMPH?
And—
GASP! WHEEZE! I'M CATCHING UP.
Then—
THIS IS MAYBE A SHEET, BUT IT'S CURTAINS FOR THEM.
EEK! I CAN'T SEE.
WHO TURNED THE LIGHTS OFF?
And—
CRUMP!
OW!
OUCH!
AH! SHAME! THEY'VE HAD A 'LITTER' ACCIDENT.
LITTER

But then—
OH, NO! THEY'RE STILL GETTING AWAY.
Suddenly—
OOPS! WHAT A TIME FOR THE SPELL TO WEAR OFF.
And—
GOLLY! DID YOU SEE THAT, INSPECTOR?
OOF!
OUCH!
URGH!
BRAKE!
THUD!
Then—
YOU CERTAINLY BROUGHT THOSE TWO DOWN TO EARTH WITH A THUD. HERE'S A REWARD.
OOH! THANKS.
Later—
THAT WAS A GREAT FEED YOU BOUGHT WITH THE REWARD MONEY, GRANDAD. NOW WOULD YOU LIKE A BIT OF SEED CAKE?
ER—NO, THANKS! I'VE GONE OFF ANYTHING TO DO WITH SEEDS.

The Hillys are a mess but far from ' armless '!

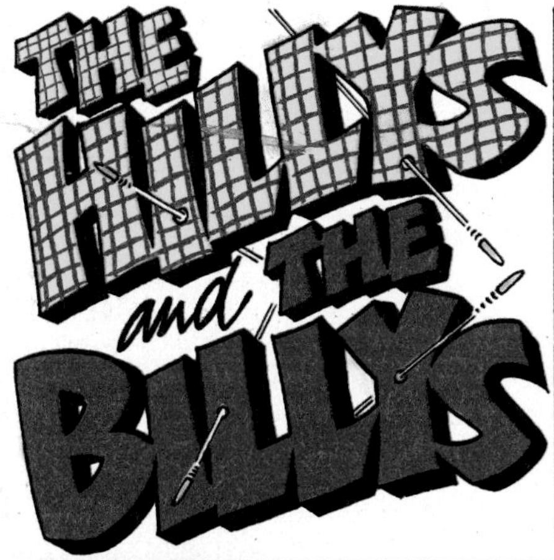

Next morning—and everyone's asleep!
ZZZ

Well, almost everyone!
WE'RE GONNA FIX THOSE BLUNDERBUSSES!
CEMENT
CEMENT

SSH! QUIETLY DOES IT!
CEMENT
CEMENT

Later—
YAH! THE BILLYS ARE SOFTIES!
WHAT'S GOIN' ON?

GRR! GRAB THE BLUNDERBUSSES, MEN!
THE BILLYS ARE BONEHEADS!
THEY DON'T SMELL TOO GOOD EITHER!

YAH! WE'RE NOT SCARED!
AIM!
WE'LL VENTILATE YOU VARMINTS.

But—
HO-HO!
HA-HA!
BANG!
BANG!
BANG!
BANG!

HO-HO! THAT IDEA WAS BANG ON!
YEAH! A SMASHING SUCCESS!

Soon after—
GRR! WE CAN'T DO ANYTHING WEARING THESE BANDAGES!
OH, NO? JUST WAIT!

Later—
LET'S GO AND PESTER THE BILLYS AGAIN!
GREAT!
GOOD IDEA!

And so—
HAR-HAR!
AW! DID YOU GET HURT, THEN?

Suddenly—
LET THEM HAVE IT, BOYS!

YOW! THEY'VE GOT PISTOLS IN THEIR BANDAGES!
WE KNEW WE'D GET YOU IN THE END.
BANG!
BANG!
BANG!
YEAH! ALL WE HAD TO DO WAS BE A LITTLE 'PATIENT'.

A laugh or two with you-know-who!

THAT DOES IT! YOU'VE ASKED FOR IT NOW.

I'LL SHOW THAT PEST!
BOWLING GREEN

GRANDAD, COULD YOU DO ME A FAVOUR..?
NNNNNNN

Soon—
I'LL BET MY GRANDAD COULD BOWL YOU OUT!
I'D LIKE TO SEE HIM TRY!

So—
A BOWLING BALL, EH? I'LL GIVE THIS A GOOD SWIPE.

But—
CRACK!
OOF!

HO-HO! WELL DONE, GRANDAD! NOT ONLY DID YOU BOWL HIM OUT—YOU BOWLED HIM OVER AS WELL!

What do you think of Baby Blink?

Baby Crockett

ME DOESN'T WANT TO BE PLUG.
PLUG

HE'S TOO UGLY FOR ME.

AHA! ME'LL JOIN THE BADD LADS.

So—
CAN ME BE A BADD LAD?
WE'LL GIVE YOU A TRIAL.
RITZ HOTEL

THERE SHOULD BE LOTS TO NICK IN THIS STREET. YOU BE THE LOOKOUT, BABY.
OKAY, BOSS.

Soon—
COME ON! WE GOT A GOOD HAUL.

But—
BAH! BUTTONS AND BADGES.
HEY! THOSE ARE MY BADGES!

WHAT A STUPID LOT. THEY ROBBED MY HOUSE!

Soon after—
WIV MY COWBOY OUTFIT, ME CAN BE JOE. NOW, ALL ME NEEDS IS A HUNGRY HOSS.

MILK
YOU LOOK LIKE A HUNGRY HOSS.
I'LL SAY.

LET'S SEE IF THERE'S ANYTHING TO EAT IN THE RANCH HOUSE.

LIKE MY MUM'S TRIFLE?
GREAT!

Suddenly—
WHAT'S GOING ON?
RUN! IT'S THE SHERIFF!

MY HORSE IS FULL UP!
AND MY LARDER IS EMPTY!
ME'LL HIDE IN THE BIN LIKE SMIFFY DOES.

I'D BETTER THROW AWAY THIS STUFF THAT THEY'VE BEEN EATING.
OH, NO!

And—
BABY! YOU'RE FILTHIER THAN SMIFFY!

Seconds later—
ME THINKS ME'LL JUST BE MYSELF. THE OTHER BEEZER PEOPLE ONLY GET ME INTO HOT WATER.

The funniest arrest in the wild and woolly West!

Soon after—

And—

And—

When Pop gets curious, the fun's fast and furious!

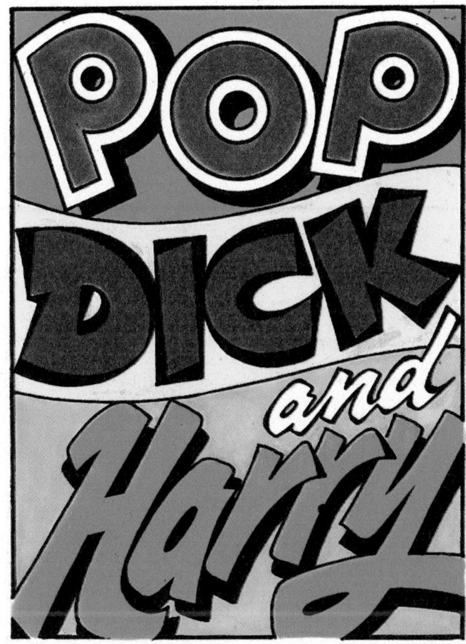

Suddenly—
YOU'LL GET A BETTER VIEW WITH THE BLINDS UP, POP!
OOYAH!

HA-HA-HA! SERVES YOU RIGHT, NOSEY PARKER!
HA-HA-HA!

Soon after—
MAYBE WE CAN CURE POP'S NOSINESS.

WE CAN USE THIS KNOT-HOLE IN THE SHED.

NOW I'LL DRILL ANOTHER TWO HOLES ABOVE IT.
I THINK I SEE WHAT YOU MEAN, HARRY.

Soon after—
BANG!
CRASH!
WALLOP!
THUMP!
I WONDER WHAT'S HAPPENING IN THE SHED. I'LL TAKE A LOOK.

But outside—
BAH! THERE'S A PIECE OF SACK OVER THE WINDOW.

HEH! I'LL LOOK THROUGH THESE KNOT-HOLES.

Then—
HELLO, POP. LOOKING FOR US?
ERK!

GRR! YOU IDIOTS! MY NOSE IS STUCK. PULL ME OUT!
OKAY, POP.

And—
OH, DEAR! THAT PLANK'S COME OFF THE SHED WITH YOU, POP.
SHAME!

OH, NO! I CAN'T GET IT OFF!
HA-HA!
HEE-HEE!

Later—
HO-HO! I'LL BET POP WON'T BE SO NOSEY AGAIN!
GRRR!

THERE'S A MAN WITH A MOUSTACHE TO SEE YOU, COLONEL.
TELL HIM I'VE ALREADY GOT ONE.

I CAN'T THINK OF ANYTHING WORSE THAN AN ELEPHANT WITH A COLD IN THE NOSE.
WHAT ABOUT A CENTIPEDE WITH CORNS?
MUSTARD

IS FIFI A GOOD WATCHDOG?
YES! ALL WE HAVE TO DO IS WAKEN HER UP AND SHE BARKS!

MUM! MUM! THE CAR'S EATING DAD!